This book belongs to

Published by
The Bible Reading Fellowship
15 The Chambers, Vineyard
Abingdon OX14 3FE
United Kingdom
Tel: +44 (0)1865 319700
Email: enquiries@brf.org.uk
Website: www.brf.org.uk
BRF is a Registered Charity

ISBN 978 0 85746 020 2

First published 2014
10 9 8 7 6 5 4 3 2 1 0

Acknowledgments

Cover photo: © Hemera/Thinkstock

Bubbles, pages 4, 5, 9, 10, 29, 32: © Hemera/Thinkstock

A catalogue record for this book is available from the British Library

Printed in the UK by Rainbow Print Wales

My Baptism Journey
Activity Book

Richard Burge, Penny Fuller and Mary Hawes

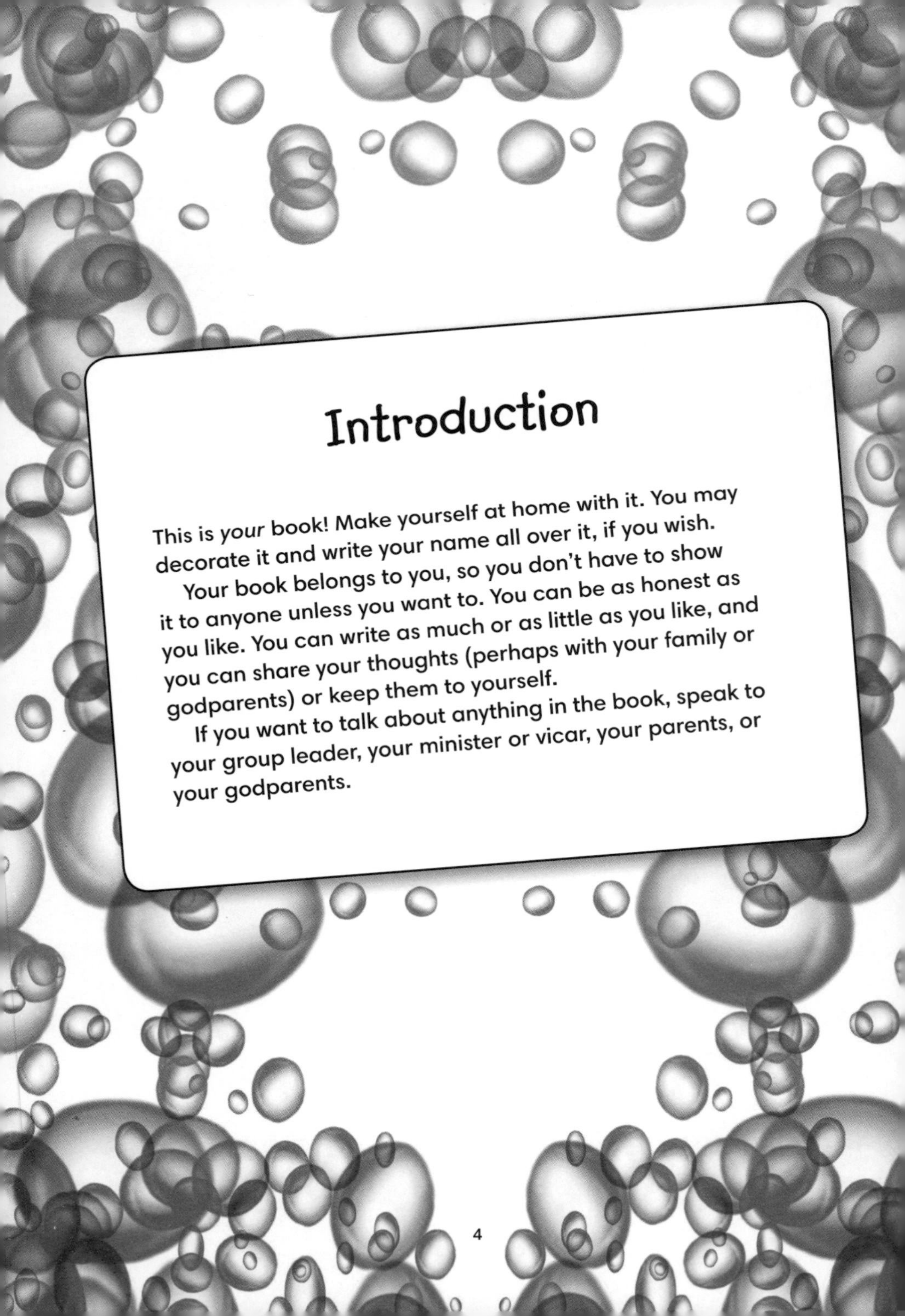

Introduction

This is *your* book! Make yourself at home with it. You may decorate it and write your name all over it, if you wish.

Your book belongs to you, so you don't have to show it to anyone unless you want to. You can be as honest as you like. You can write as much or as little as you like, and you can share your thoughts (perhaps with your family or godparents) or keep them to yourself.

If you want to talk about anything in the book, speak to your group leader, your minister or vicar, your parents, or your godparents.

Colour wheel

At the back of the book there is a colour wheel. If you are asked a question about how you feel, sometimes it can be hard to put your feelings into words. The colour wheel helps you to describe your feelings in terms of colours. The 'warm colours' (red, orange, yellow) might make us feel warm or hot when we look at them; they might also make us feel active, energised or excited. The 'cool colours' (green, blue, violet) might make us feel cold when we look at them; they might also make us feel relaxed, calm or peaceful. Test out the colour wheel by listing a few natural things that have 'cold' colours (that make us feel cold) or 'warm' colours (that make us feel warm).

Throughout your journal there are questions and opportunities to reflect on what you have experienced. Each time, look at your colour wheel and choose a colour that seems to stand out to you at that moment. Then try to write down how you feel, or colour in the colour.

What colour are you immediately drawn to? How does the colour make you feel?

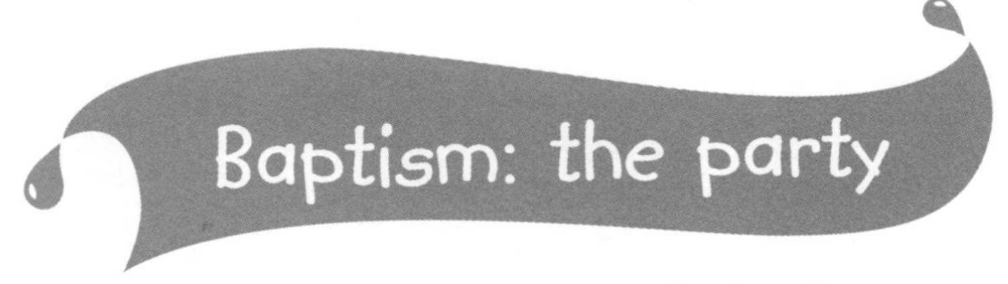

This activity book can help you to explore what baptism means. Someone may have given you this book because:

- your little brother or sister is being christened/baptised;
- you have asked questions about being christened/baptised and want to find out more.

There may be words in this book that you do not recognise—words that are often used in church. If you come across any words that you don't fully understand, check out the 'Key words' list on page 31.

Words to look out for

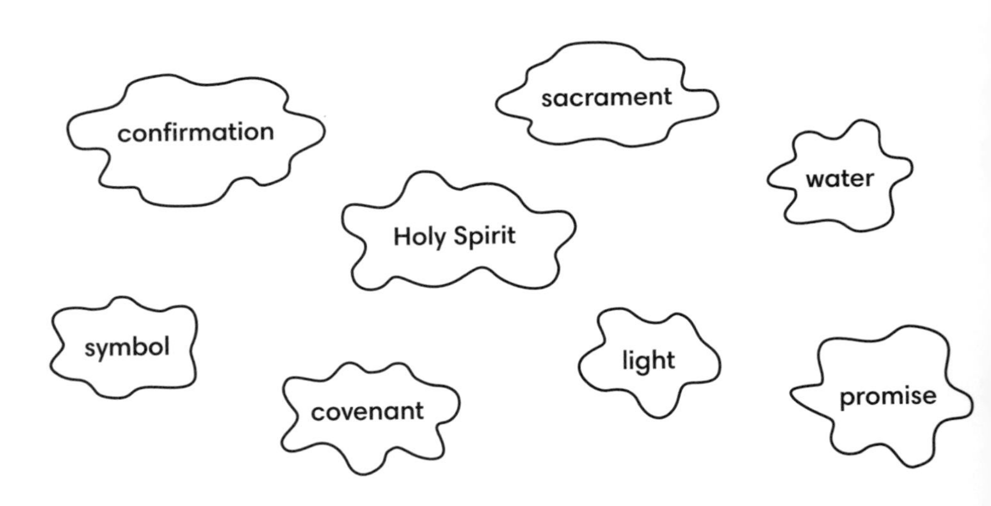

At a baptism, people usually invite friends and family to join them at the church service and at a party afterwards. The whole of baptism is a celebration—one big party with your friends, family, the church and God, all celebrating the promises they are making. Later on, we will look at the promises in more detail.

Who is being baptised?

- ☐ Is it you?
- ☐ Is it your baby brother or sister?
- ☐ Or is it a friend of the family?

If it is your brother or sister who is being baptised, stick a picture of them here, with their godparent(s), your parent(s), you and any other sibling(s) you have.

If you don't have photographs, draw pictures!

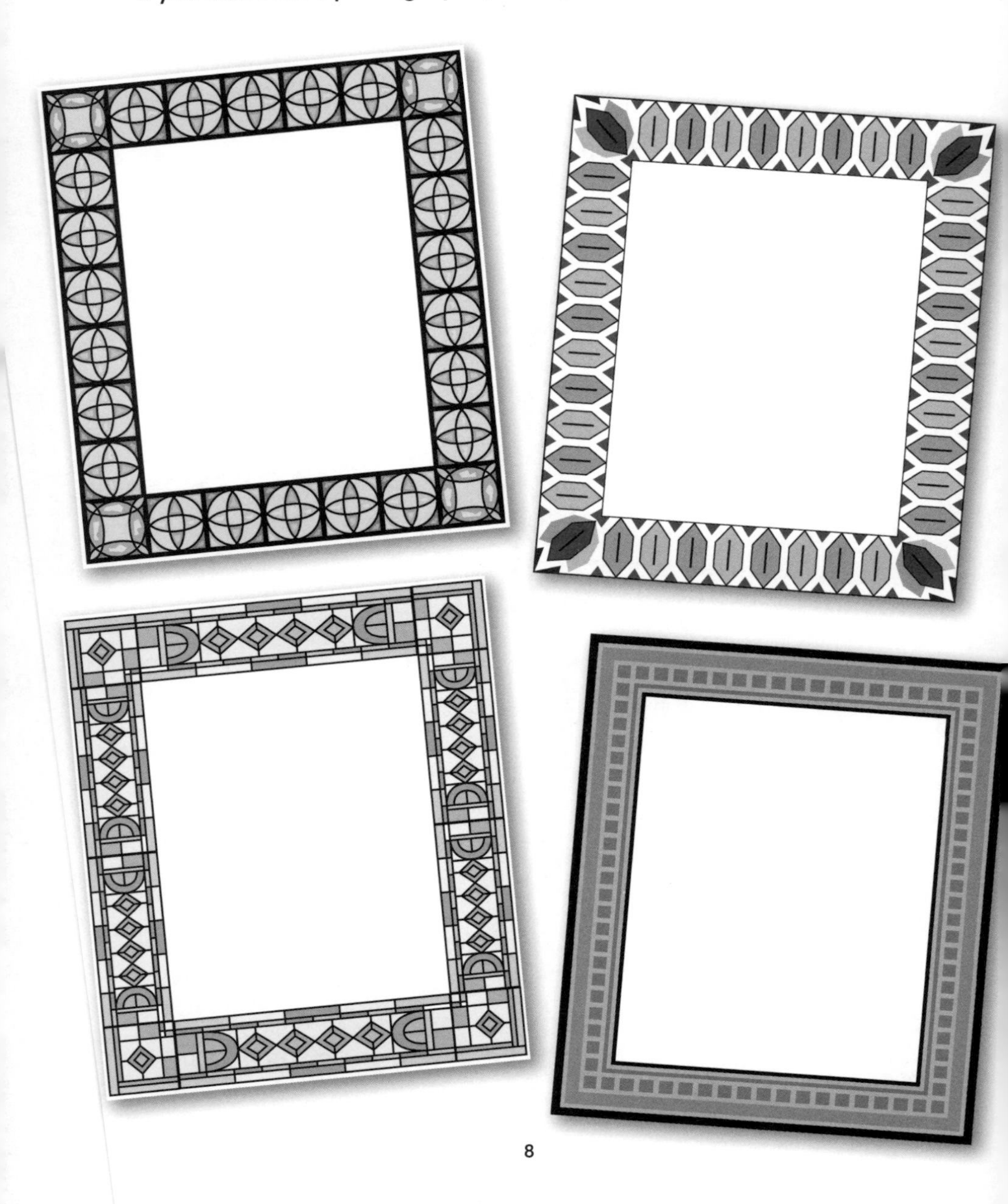

Memory box

Ask your parent(s)/guardian(s) about their baptisms (or the baptisms of people they know)—whether they were babies, children, teenagers or adults when they were baptised. What special clothes were worn? What special gifts were received? What special words were said?

Write their answers here:

Show them the colour wheel inside the back cover. Ask them to choose a colour that expresses how they feel about the memory.

Your questions!

What questions do you want to ask about baptism? Write them down here:

Who will you ask to answer your questions, and when will you ask them?

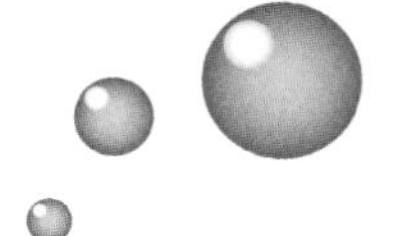

Here are some Bible passages that you can look up about baptism:

If you don't have a Bible, you could try to search for the passage on the internet. Or, if your parents or godparents have a tablet or smartphone, ask them to download a Bible app for you.

Draw a picture here to illustrate the Bible passages, or rewrite them in your own words.

Who are the godparents of your parent(s)/guardian(s)?
Are those godparents still involved in their lives?
Who have your parents chosen to be your or your sibling's godparents?
Why did they choose those people?
Who would you choose to be your godparents? Why?
Who will be the guests at the baptism?

Design an invitation to send to your family and friends, inviting them to the baptism.

What has this section made you think about?

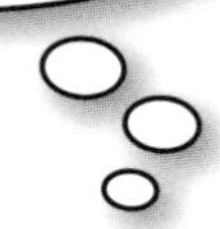

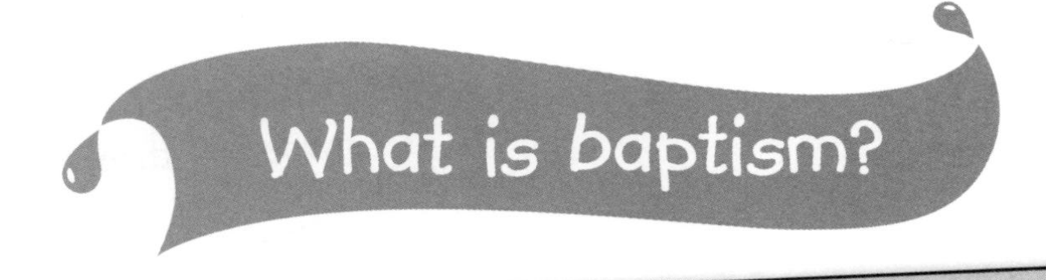

What is baptism?

Fill in the blank spaces in the sentences below. First, you will need to unscramble the words below the lines to help you complete the sentences.

Baptism is a _ _ _ _ _ _ _ _ _ _ . It is a _ _ _ _ _ _ _
to God and an invitation to join the _ _ _ _ _ _ .
It is also a promise from _ _ _ .

TASCMRANE ESIROMP HURCHC DGO

Answers: SACRAMENT, PROMISE, CHURCH, GOD

A special ceremony

In order to thank God for their child, many parents have a special ceremony to welcome their child into the church family. This ceremony is called baptism.

Not all babies are baptised. Some parents prefer to wait for the child to make their own decision about religion and faith; some may not think it is necessary; others just don't get round to doing it. If you weren't baptised as a baby (or if you were dedicated instead of being baptised), you can choose to be baptised.

Baptism is a sacrament—a gift from God, in which ordinary things such as water are given a special and holy significance. When someone is baptised, Christians publicly celebrate the love of God and welcome them into the church.

Can you unscramble the words to find out some of the gifts of baptism?

CEGRA HCCRUH SAVTLAONI ELVO FO DGO

Answers: GRACE, CHURCH, SALVATION, LOVE OF GOD

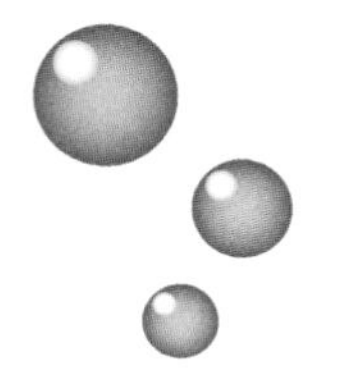

Who can be baptised and what do they do?

Infant baptism (baby)

The parent(s) promise(s) to guide their child in faith.

A person (parents, godparents) promises to live a life of faith.

The church promises to guide the child on their discipleship journey.

Someone (the baby or child—the 'candidate') is welcomed as part of the Christian family.

Someone (parents, godparents) accepts God's gift of grace on behalf of the baby.

Child (if you make the decision to be baptised yourself) or adult baptism

Godparents promise to guide you and teach you about God.

Someone (the 'candidate') accepts faith in God.

Someone (the 'candidate') makes a commitment to follow God.

More questions and answers

What's the difference between a baptism and a christening?

None. They are just different words for the same thing.

What is a godparent?

Godparents are usually chosen by the parent(s) from among their friends or relatives. Godparents promise to pray and support the child and to help the parent(s) to bring up the child in the Christian faith. If you are the person being baptised, you could help to choose who your godparent(s) will be.

How many godparents should there be?

There is no set number, but most people have two or three godparents.

What is the baptism service?

This is a sacrament and a celebration. During the service, if a newborn baby is being baptised, they cannot make the promises themselves, so their parent(s)/guardian(s)/godparent(s) and the church make the promises for them. If you are being baptised as a child or adult, you make promises to God yourself.

What has this section made you think about?

What happens at a baptism service?

Promises made at a baptism

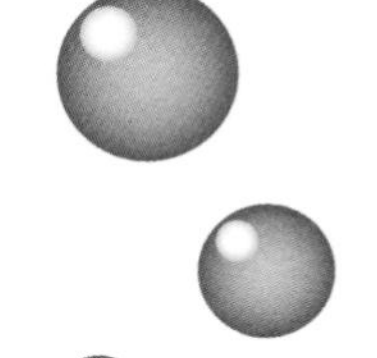

THE CHURCH promises to enable children to grow in the knowledge and love of God.

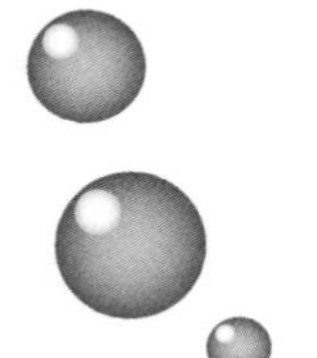

PARENTS promise to pray for and with their children, and to guide and encourage the child who is being baptised.

GODPARENTS promise to support the parents in all this, and to support the child on their faith journey.

IF YOU ARE BEING BAPTISED, you make the promises to God yourself.

Symbols we use in the baptism service

THE SYMBOL OF WATER: At the baptism, the minister pours water on to the baby's head (or your head, if you are being baptised) in the name of the Father, the Son and the Holy Spirit. This is a sign of new life.

Think about all the things water is used for.
Now write a poem in the box about water:

Or

draw three different pictures that describe or show what we use water for.

THE SIGN OF THE CROSS: The minister/vicar makes the sign of the cross on the forehead of the baby (or, if you are being baptised, on your forehead), as a sign that the child (or you) now belongs to God.

Use the colour wheel inside the back cover to choose colours that express how you feel about knowing that you belong to God.

Write a letter to God about what it is like to be a child.

THE SYMBOL OF THE CANDLE: At a baptismal service, a lighted candle may be given to the parents or siblings of the baby/child who is being baptised. This is a symbol of Christ, who is the light of the world.

Where do you see God in our world? Design a special poster to show your answer.

THE WELCOME OF THE CHURCH: At a baptism, a child is welcomed into the family of the church.

How many words can you make out of the letters W E L C O M E? List them below.

What has this section made you think about?

On the baptism day

How can I be involved in the christening/baptism?

If it is the baptism of your baby brother or sister:

You could ask to read or write some special prayers.

You could choose or write a poem for the baby and read it out in the service.

You could pour the water into the font during the ceremony.

You could hold the lit candle, given to the baby to represent Christ, the light of the world.

You could introduce the baby to members of your church.

You could write a letter to the baby, describing how the day went.

If it is your baptism:

You could share with the congregation why God is important in your life.

You will make the promises to God during the baptism service.

You could read a passage from the Bible that means something to you.

You could write a prayer or poem for the service.

You could make a short video asking the church questions about God.

Look at the baptism pictures:
What do they tell you about baptism?
Which picture do you prefer, and why?
What symbols can you see in the pictures?

What has this section made you think about?

Any further questions?

If you have any more questions you would like to ask the minister/vicar about baptism, write them here.

If you have any more questions you would like to ask your parent(s) about baptism, write them here.

Write in your own words what you think baptism is about.
I think baptism is:
You may wish to use this space to write or draw a prayer to God.

Key words

- BAPTISM: A Christian ceremony that involves sprinkling water on someone (or sometimes fully immersing someone in water) and welcoming them into the Christian family.
- CEREMONY: A formal occasion such as a wedding or a baptism, at which special things are said and done.
- CHRISTENING: Like baptism, a Christian ceremony to welcome a baby into the Christian family.
- COMMITMENT: A strong belief in something, shown by a promise to do something.
- CONFIRMATION: A special Christian ceremony to welcome a person into the Christian family, usually an adult who was christened as a child.
- COVENANT: In baptism, this is another word for a promise or mutual agreement made between a person and God.
- FONT: The vessel that holds the water for the baptism. In some churches, the font can be a large, very old stone vessel.
- GODPARENTS: People who are invited to be part of the child's life by the parents or the child themselves. They have a special role in helping the child to grow as a Christian. They promise to support the child and their parents in their journey of faith.
- GRACE: The term used for God's help when it is given to humans.
- HOLY SPIRIT: The third person of the Christian Trinity. The other two are (1) God the Father and (2) Jesus, God the Son. God as Spirit, sometimes called the Counsellor, descended on Jesus 'like a dove' at his baptism and also comes to be with us and guide us when we become a Christian.
- INFANT BAPTISM: A Christian ceremony to welcome a baby into the Christian family.
- MINISTER: A church leader such as a vicar, pastor or priest.
- SACRAMENT: A spiritual symbol, believed to be a sign of God's grace.
- SYMBOL: Something that represents something else. For example, in baptism, the lit candle represents Jesus, the light of the world.

The colour wheel

Look at the colour wheel when you are thinking hard about a subject.

Pick a colour that best suits your thoughts on a topic.

Is it a warm colour or a cool colour, or perhaps something in between?

What words would you use to describe this colour?

When and how does your colour choice change?